M000198403

# THE
# SONG
# OF
# OUR
# SYRIAN
# GUEST

# THE SONG OF OUR SYRIAN GUEST

BY WILLIAM ALLEN KNIGHT

THE PILGRIM PRESS

NEW YORK

**Library of Congress Cataloging in
Publication Data**

Knight, William Allen, 1863-1957
   The song of our Syrian guest.

   1. Bible.   O.T.   Psalms XXIII — Criticism,
interpretation, etc.   1. Title.
[BS1450.23d.K6   1972]      223'.2      72-4580
ISBN 0-8298-0834-5

TO THE HAND
THAT HELD THE TEA-BALL
AND THE FACES
OF THE TWO LITTLE MAIDS

# CONTENTS

# INTRODUCTION

For nearly seven decades *The Song of Our Syrian Guest* has given spiritual insight and inspiration to many persons. Its impact has been very large indeed, for over two million copies are now in print. Its lyrical, sometimes mystical, story seems to earn a hearing with each new generation and age.

If, as has been suggested, we have entered a new age in recent years, then it is a propitious and fitting time for a new edition of *The Song of Our Syrian Guest*. This is not so much because the story speaks of another time and place, but because in speaking of them it speaks about all times, all places, and all people.

*The Song of Our Syrian Guest* is a story infused with a single-minded understanding of the earth. The often ignored realities of the earth are profound: stones and trees, plants and animals, the

11

flow of waters, the rhythm of days and nights, the interdependent lives of sheep and shepherds. These realities are profound in their simplicity and thus they have much to offer to us in this new age. This is a story of simplicity in which there is a *vision* and a *hope*. In a way, its simplicity *is* its vision and its hope, for "it is all, all a simple shepherd psalm."

Reading the shepherd psalm generates new thoughts just as it can provide comfort and support for the weary, the confused, and the distressed of the earth. In its vision there is abundant hope. This vision and hope of the earth speaks to the human search for identity and wholeness. It offers a vision of goodness and mercy. Experiencing goodness and mercy seems inevitably to involve coming close to the enduring things of the earth. And to inhabit the earth for even a brief time is to receive the chance to experience these things or to deny them. Certainly in this new age experiencing goodness and mercy is as needed as it has been in other ages. The simple shepherd song is a way to begin that experiencing. And inevitably it is so much more, for goodness and mercy are many sided, even as they endure forever.

The Publisher

# FOREWORD

A Godspeed is fitting as a pilgrim after much journeying fares forth once more; and such is this little book. Of the memories that hover about the pen writing these lines, one only may have place on the page. It is of a day when this word came from a mountain village: "It has shown me the shepherd as a savior and the Savior as a Shepherd." Because some who will look upon these pages are in sick rooms, some are lonely, being companioned only by grief, some are poor and some for the time are misunderstood, some are rich and allured by many voices, some are discouraged and feel that they are little loved, some are young and cannot find their way, and some are old and wayworn—because all have need of the Shepherd's care, go, little Book, once more, bearing this token only.

William Allen Knight

# THE TWENTY-THIRD PSALM

THE LORD IS MY SHEPHERD; I SHALL NOT WANT. HE MAKETH ME TO LIE DOWN IN GREEN PASTURES: HE LEAD– ETH ME BESIDE THE STILL WATERS. HE RESTORETH MY SOUL: HE LEADETH ME IN THE PATHS OF RIGHTEOUSNESS FOR HIS NAME'S SAKE. YEA, THOUGH I WALK THROUGH THE VALLEY OF THE SHADOW OF DEATH, I WILL FEAR NO EVIL: FOR THOU ART WITH ME; THY ROD AND THY STAFF THEY COMFORT ME. THOU PREPAREST A TABLE BE– FORE ME IN THE PRESENCE OF MINE ENEMIES: THOU ANOINTEST MY HEAD WITH OIL; MY CUP RUNNETH OVER. SURELY GOODNESS AND MERCY SHALL FOLLOW ME ALL THE DAYS OF MY LIFE AND I WILL DWELL IN THE HOUSE OF THE LORD FOREVER.

# THE SONG OF OUR SYRIAN GUEST

"Faduel Moghabghab," said our guest, laughing as he leaned over the tea-table toward two little maids, vainly trying to beguile their willing and sweetly puckered lips into pronouncing his name. "Faduel Moghabghab," he repeated in syllables, pointing to the card he had passed to them. "Accent the u and drop those g's which your little throats cannot manage," he went on kindly, while the merriment sparkled in his lustrous dark eyes, and his milk-white teeth, seen through his black moustache as he laughed, added beauty to his delicate and vivacious face.

He was a man of winsome mind, this Syrian guest of ours, and the spirituality of his culture was as marked as the refinement of his manners. We shall long remember him for the tales told that evening of his home in Ainzehalta on the slope of the Syrian mountains, but longest of all for what he said out of the memories of his youth about a shepherd song.

"It was out of the shepherd life of my country," he remarked, "that there came long ago that sweetest religious song ever written—the Twenty-third Psalm."

After the ripple of his merriment with the children had passed he turned to me with a face now serious and pensive, and said: "Ah, so many things familiar to us are strange to you of America."

"Yes," I answered, "and no doubt because of this we often make mistakes which are more serious than mispronunciation of your names."

He smiled pleasantly, then with earnestness said: "So many things in the life of my people, the same now as in the days of old, have been woven into the words of the Bible and into the religious ideas expressed there; you of the Western world, not knowing these things as they are, often misunderstand what is written, or at least fail to get a correct impression from it."

"Tell us about some of these," I ventured, with a parental glance at two listening little faces.

After mentioning several instances, he went on: "And there is the shepherd psalm; I find that it is taken among you as having two parts, the first under the figure of shepherd life, the second turning to the scene of a banquet with the host and the guest."

"Oh, we have talked about that," said my lady of the teacups as she dangled the tea-ball with a connoisseur's fondness, "and we have even said that we wished the wonderful little psalm could have been finished in the one figure of shepherd life."

"It seems to us," I added, wishing to give suitable support to my lady's rather brave declaration of our sense of a literary flaw in the matchless psalm, "it seems to us to lose the sweet, simple melody and to close with strange, heavy chords when it changes to a scene of banquet hospitality. Do you mean that it actually keeps the shepherd figure to the end?"

"Certainly, good friends."

With keen personal interest I asked him to tell us how we might see it as a shepherd psalm throughout. So we listened, and he talked, over the cooling teacups.

"It is all, all a simple shepherd psalm," he began. "See how it runs through the round of shepherd life from first word to last."

With softly modulated voice that had the rhythm of music and the hush of veneration in it, he quoted: "'THE LORD IS MY SHEP-HERD; I SHALL NOT WANT.'"

"There is the opening strain of its music; in that chord is sounded the keynote which is never lost till the plaintive melody dies away at the song's end. All that follows is that thought put in varying light."

I wish it were possible to reproduce here the light in his face and the interchange of tones in his mellow voice as he went on. He talked of how the varied needs of the sheep and the many-sided care of the shepherd are pictured in the short sentences of the psalm.

"Each is distinct and adds something too precious to be merged and lost," he said.

"'HE MAKETH ME TO LIE DOWN IN GREEN PASTURES,'—nourishment, rest. 'HE LEADETH ME BESIDE THE STILL WATERS,'—the scene changes and so does the meaning. You think here of quietly flowing streams; so you get one more picture of rest; but you miss one of the finest scenes in shepherd life and one of the rarest blessings of the soul that is led of God. All through the day's roaming the shepherd keeps one thing in mind. He must lead his flock to a drinking-place. The refreshment of good water marks the coveted hour of all the day; the spot where it is found amid the rough, waterless hills and plains is the crowning token of the shepherd's unfailing thoughtfulness. When at last the sheep are led 'BESIDE THE STILL WATERS,' how good it is, after the dust and heat of the sheep-walks!

"But what would a shepherd mean by those words, 'HE LEADETH ME BESIDE THE STILL WATERS'? You know of rivers and brooks in the Holy Land, for their names are read many times in the Bible; but you do not think how the rivers are far from each other through rough country; and you know not how many of the brooks are called 'wadies' by us because they are only ravines that run dry when the rainy season ends. Job says, 'My brethren have dealt deceitfully as a brook, as the channel of brooks that pass away.' In the region where

David was a shepherd living streams are scarce indeed; for Judea borders on the south country called Negeb and that means 'the dry.' Even in other parts where the lasting streams are, how often the shepherd finds them in gullies between broken hills, how often the banks are too dangerous for the sheep and the flow too rough. Sheep are timid and fear a current of water, as they well may, for they are easily carried down stream because of their wool."

"Poor things, how do they ever get a good drink!" exclaimed one of the two little maids, whose heart was always open lovingly to animals.

"The shepherd sees to that, doesn't he?" said the other timidly, with earnest eyes set on our guest.

His face beamed with winsome relish of these tributes to his success. "Yes, the sheep would indeed have a hard time finding water to drink, were it not that the shepherd sees to that."

25

The playfulness faded from his eyes and the shadow of manhood's years was there as he said to me: "Brother, you and I have learned how much is in that question and answer. How should we get the refreshment we need in the rough world, if the Shepherd did not see to that? But he does, he does!"

His face brightened again as he turned to the four blue eyes across the table.

"Shall I tell you how the shepherd sees to it that the sheep have a good drink every day? Listen.

"There are wells and fountains at many points in the regions where the flocks roam, and in some parts there are cisterns, though the sheep like the living water best. The shepherds know where these drinking-places are all through the country where streams are few. It is a fine sight to see the shepherds bring their flocks 'BESIDE THE STILL WATERS' at some well or fountain, while the wide, silent country, over which they and many other sheep have wandered, spreads all around them, and the far expanse of the sky arches over them.

"The shepherd makes a certain sound; all his sheep lie down and are quiet. Then he fills the drinking-troughs. The bubbling of the fountain, or the current, if it be by a stream, is no longer there to trouble the sheep. They can drink now undisturbed. This is the delicate meaning of that word 'still.' As the Hebrew words put it, 'He leadeth beside the waters of quietness.'

"Then the waiting sheep hear a whistle or a call. They never misunderstand; they know their shepherd's voice and never respond to the wrong shepherd if several flocks have come up together. And, strangest of all, the sheep come up by groups; the shepherd makes them understand. So in groups he leads them until they stand 'BESIDE THE STILL WATERS.' And, oh, how they drink, with the shepherd standing near!"

After a pause, with a far-off look in his eyes, he said, "It is a beautiful scene, so beautiful that St. John has used it in picturing heaven." A smile broke over his face as he quoted: "'The Lamb that is in the midst of the throne shall be their shepherd, and shall guide them unto fountains of waters of life.'"

No one spoke as he sat turning his teacup. A tear started from his downcast eyes. Presently he seemed to recall himself.

"But I must tell you of one more scene that comes to my memory whenever I read the words, 'HE LEADETH ME BESIDE THE STILL WATERS.' It would make a beautiful picture if some one would paint it.

"Up in the mountainsides of Lebanon, where my kinsmen have long been shepherds, often there are no regular drinking-places, such as the wells and fountains on the plains. But as the shepherd leads his sheep over the rough slopes, he finds many a spring and sees its rivulet noisily running down a crevice. His sheep need water. They cannot drink from the leaping little stream. What does he do? He finds a suitable turn or nook in its course; he walls it up with a little dam and so holds the water till it forms a quiet pool. Then, right there on the open hills, he leads his sheep 'BESIDE THE STILL WATERS,' which the shepherd's own hand has stilled. I know of nothing more fit to picture the Shepherd's care of souls that trust him than that scene up there on the mountainside.''

While our thoughts were carried away to these scenes of thirsty flocks drinking, I chanced to notice that the tea-ball was again quietly at work. As we sat thinking on that picture up in the mountain, a good hand offered our guest a fresh cup. He received it with a low bow, sipped it in quiet, then with a grateful smile began speaking again.

"'HE RESTORETH MY SOUL.' You know," he said, turning to me, "that soul means the life or one's own self in the Hebrew writings."

Then addressing us all he went on: "There are perilous places for the sheep on all sides, and they seem never to learn to avoid them. The shepherd must ever be on the watch. And there are private fields and sometimes gardens and vineyards here and there in the shepherd country; if a sheep stray into them and be caught there it is forfeited to the owner of the land. So, 'HE RESTORETH MY SOUL' means, 'The shepherd brings me back and rescues me from fatal and forbidden places.'"

"'Restores me when wandering,' is the way it is put in one of our hymns," I interposed.

"Ah, sir, that is it exactly," he answered, "'Restores me when wandering!'

"'HE LEADETH ME IN THE PATHS OF RIGHTEOUSNESS FOR HIS NAME'S SAKE.' Often have I roamed through the shepherd country in my youth and seen how hard it is to choose the right path for the sheep; one leads to a precipice, another to a place where the sheep cannot find the way back; and the shepherd was always going ahead, 'leading' them in the right paths, proud of his good name as a shepherd.

"Some paths that are right paths still lead through places that have deadly perils. 'YEA, THOUGH I WALK THROUGH THE VAL-LEY OF THE SHADOW OF DEATH,' is the way the psalm touches this fact in shepherd life. This way of naming the valley is very true to our country. I remember one near my home called 'the valley of robbers,' and another, 'the

31

ravine of the raven.' You see 'the valley of the shadow of death' is a name drawn from my country's old custom.

"'FOR THOU ART WITH ME.' Ah, how could more be put into few words! With the sheep, it matters not what the surroundings are, nor how great the perils and hardships; if only the shepherd is with them, they are content. There is no finer picture of the way of peace for the troubled in all the world.

"To show how much the presence of the shepherd counts for the welfare of the sheep I can think of nothing better than the strange thing I now tell you. It is quite beyond the usual, daily care on which the flock depends so fondly. But I have seen it more than once.

"Sometimes, in spite of all the care of the shepherd and his dogs, a wolf will get into the very midst of the flock. The sheep are wild with fright. They run and leap and make it impossible to get at the foe in their midst, who at that very moment may be fastening his fangs in the throat of a helpless member of the flock. But the shepherd is with them. He knows what to do even at such a time. He leaps to a rock or hillock that he may be seen and heard. Then he lifts his voice in a long call, something like a wolf's cry: 'Ooh! ooh!'

"On hearing this the sheep remember the shepherd; they heed his voice; and, strange to tell, the poor, timid creatures, which were helpless with terror before, instantly rush with all their strength into a solid mass. The pressure is irresistible; the wolf is overcome; frequently he is crushed to death, while the shepherd stands there on a rock crying, 'Ooh! ooh!' 'I WILL FEAR NO EVIL: FOR THOU ART WITH ME.'"

He paused, looking questioningly at one and another.

"Yes," I said at last, "'in all these things we are more than conquerors through him that loved us.'" He bowed his satisfaction in silence.

"'THY ROD AND THY STAFF'—this also is true to life; the double expression covers the whole round of protecting care. For the shepherds carry a crook for guiding the sheep and a weapon suitable for defending them, the staff and the rod; one for aiding them in places of need along peaceful ways, the other for defense in perils of robbers and wild beasts. This saying describes as only a shepherd could how much those words mean, 'THOU ART WITH ME.'

"And what shall I say of the next words, 'THEY COMFORT ME'? Ah, madam, you should see the sheep cuddle near the shepherd to understand that! The shepherd's call, 'Ta-a-a-a, ho-o-o,' and the answering patter of feet as the sheep hurry to him are fit sounds to be chosen out of the noisy world to show what comfort God gives to souls that heed his voice; and those sounds have been heard in my country this day as they were the day this shepherd psalm was written!"

He sat in silence a moment, musing as if the sounds were in his ear.

With quiet animation he lifted his thin hand and continued: "Now here is where you drop the shepherd figure and put in a banquet and so lose the fine climax of completeness in the shepherd's care."

It need not be said that we were eager listeners now, for our guest was all aglow with memories of his far-off homeland and we felt that we were about to see new rays of light flash from this rarest gem in the song-treasury of the world.

"THOU PREPAREST A TABLE BEFORE ME IN THE PRESENCE OF MINE ENE-MIES." In the same hushed voice in which he quoted these words he added: "Ah, to think that the shepherd's highest skill and heroism should be lost from view as the psalm begins to sing of it, and only an indoor banquet thought of!" Again he sat a little time in quiet. Then he said:

"The word for table here used simply means something 'spread out.' One of the psalms quotes the saying, 'Can God prepare a table in the wilderness?' In olden times the table in our country was often just what you see to this day among the Arabs, only a piece of skin or a mat or a cloth spread on the ground. That shows what is meant when the psalmist says, 'Let their table become a snare; and when they are at peace let it become a trap.' Do you not see? He was thinking of this way of having meals on the ground in the open country, and wished that his enemies might be caught off guard while eating and entangled among the things that were spread before them. This is the kind of table that would be thought of in shepherd life. Why not so in a shepherd song?

"Now is not that exactly like what the shepherd prepares for his sheep? Along with finding water he has the daily task of searching out a good and safe feeding-place. He 'prepares a table before them' in truth, and it is none the less a table in his eyes because it is a spreading slope of grassy ground.

"All the shepherd's skill and often heroic work are called forth in this duty, for it is done many a day 'in the presence of the sheep's enemies.' There are many poisonous plants in the grass and the shepherd must find and avoid them. The sheep will not eat certain poisonous things, but there are some which they will eat, one kind of poisonous grass in particular. A cousin of mine once lost three hundred sheep by a mistake in this hard task.

"Then there are snake holes in some kinds of ground, and, if the snakes be not driven away, they bite the noses of the sheep. For this the shepherd sometimes burns the fat of hogs along the ground. Sometimes he finds ground where moles have worked their holes just under the surface. Snakes lie in these holes with their heads sticking up ready to bite the grazing sheep. The shepherd knows how to drive them away as he goes along ahead of the sheep.

"And around the feeding-ground which the shepherd thus prepares, in holes and caves in the hillsides there may be jackals, wolves, hyenas, and panthers, too, and the bravery and skill of the shepherd are at the highest point in closing up these dens with stones or slaying the wild beasts with his long-bladed knife. Of nothing do you hear shepherds boasting more proudly than of their achievements in this part of their care of flocks.

"And now," exclaimed our guest with a beaming countenance and suppressed feeling, as if pleading for recognition of the lone shepherd's bravest act of devotion to his sheep, "and now do you not see the shepherd meaning in that quaint line, 'THOU PREPAREST A TABLE BEFORE ME IN THE PRESENCE OF MINE ENEMIES'?"

"Yes," I answered; "and I see that God's care of a man out in the world means far more for his good than seating him at an indoor banquet-table!

"But what about anointing the head with oil and the cup running over? Go on, my friend."

"Oh, there begins the beautiful picture at the end of the day. The psalm has sung of the whole round of the day's wandering, all the needs of the sheep, all the care of the shepherd. Now it closes with the last scene of the day. At the door of the sheepfold the shepherd stands and 'the rodding of the sheep' takes place. The shepherd turns his body to let the sheep pass; he is the door, as Christ said of himself. With his rod he holds back the sheep while he looks them over one by one as they go into the fold. He has the horn filled with olive-oil and he has cedar-tar, and he anoints a knee bruised on the rocks or a side scratched by thorns. And here comes one that is not bruised but is simply worn and exhausted; he bathes its face and head with the refreshing olive-oil and he takes the large two-handled cup and dips it brimming full from the water he has brought for that purpose, and he lets the weary sheep drink.

"There is nothing finer in the psalm than this. God's care is not for the wounded only; it is for those who are just worn and weary. 'THOU ANOINTEST MY HEAD WITH OIL; MY CUP RUNNETH OVER.'

"And then, when the day is done and the

sheep are snug within the fold, what contentment, what rest under the starry sky! Then comes the thought of deepest repose and comfort: 'SURELY GOODNESS AND MERCY SHALL FOLLOW ME ALL THE DAYS OF MY LIFE,' as they have through all the wandering of the day now ended.

"As the song dies away the heart that God has watched and tended breathes this thought of peace before the roaming of the day is forgotten in sleep: 'I WILL DWELL IN THE HOUSE OF THE LORD FOREVER.' The song is hushed, and the sheep are at rest, safe in the good shepherd's fold."

Do you wonder that ever since that night we have called this psalm The Song of Our Syrian Guest?

# EPILOGUE

Forty years have gone by since *The Song of Our Syrian Guest* completed its story out of shepherd life with the scene of comfort and peace at the day's end—forty years since this child of my love in the long ago began telling its story near and far.

How many, the world over, have welcomed it for what it told them about their dearest song of trust!

It seems strange that now, having itself become a veteran also, it has come back from such a pilgrimage to receive, as it were, a father's benediction. Can it be, after all these years, that any words of mine may add some further touch of blessing to what God gave this little book long ago?

Amid these times of trial for multitudes that

no man can number, there came a happening which cleared away my misgivings.

One evening I went through a peaceful countryside to a village church, wondering why a distinguished clergyman was coming from a great metropolitan ministry to speak in a quiet old village—and in a church outside the usual range of his churchmanship.*

As the noted preacher, still in the strength of later mid-life, poured forth a plea for direct personal reliance on God in all life conditions, I soon began taking notes, so masterful was the simplicity of his thought and its wording.

He could have known nothing of the stranger well back in the full pews—certainly nothing of the reason for the eagerness that speeded my pencil when, at length, his voice took on a hush

*Dean Edwin J. van Etten, of St. Paul's Cathedral, Boston.

and his face a radiance as he said: "See how reliance on the care divine in all conditions of life
is shown in that matchless song of trust, the
Shepherd Psalm."

Came then this unforgettable outshowing of
a charm deftly inlaid in the words of the wonderful little psalm which, once seen, is as clear
as a string of priceless pearls:

With what simplicity the deepening of trust
as the need deepens is voiced in the change of
pronouns! At first, in life's pleasant places,
the Lord is spoken of—four times "He" is
acknowledged as the giver of all comforts and
joys. But in the dark and dangerous places,
the Lord is spoken to—the trusting heart
there says "Thou" and "Thy"—does so four
times, the same as when life was peaceful in
green pastures and beside still waters. This is
the fullness of meaning in those crowning

words—"goodness and mercy shall follow me all the days of my life"—all the days!

Go, little book, once more, bearing to all who need and will receive it this further blessing. How strange it seems that it was given to me to receive this treasure of words through the voice of a stranger, after forty years!

As life's long day is turning toward evening for me, let this be your evensong—closing the ministries of all your days to come.